# MyWorkBook
# Sample Chapter

## Preview for the
# Bittinger Worktext Series

## Marvin L. Bittinger
*Indiana University Purdue University Indianapolis*

## David J. Ellenbogen
*Community College of Vermont*

## Judith A. Beecher
*Indiana University Purdue University Indianapolis*

## Judith A. Penna
*Indiana University Purdue University Indianapolis*

## Barbara L. Johnson
*Indiana University Purdue University Indianapolis*

**Addison-Wesley**
is an imprint of

PEARSON

Copyright © 2012 Pearson Education, Inc.
Publishing as Pearson Addison-Wesley, 75 Arlington Street, Boston, MA 02116.

ISBN-13: 978-0-321-76263-4
ISBN-10: 0-321-76263-0

1 2 3 4 5 6 BB 14 13 12 11 10

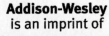

**Addison-Wesley**
is an imprint of

www.pearsonhighered.com

# Chapter 1 WHOLE NUMBERS

## 1.1 Standard Notation

**Learning Objectives**
A   Give the meaning of digits in standard notation.
B   Convert from standard notation to expanded notation.
C   Convert between standard notation and word names.

**Key Terms**
Use the vocabulary terms listed below to complete each statement in Exercises 1–5.

| | | |
|---|---|---|
| **natural** | **whole** | **digit** |
| **standard** | **expanded** | |

1.   The number 5 thousands + 4 hundreds + 9 tens + 2 ones is expressed in _____ notation.

2.   The set 0, 1, 2, 3, 4,... is the set of _____ numbers.

3.   A _____ is a number 0, 1, 2, 3, 4, 5, 6, 7, 8, or 9 that names a place-value location.

4.   The set 1, 2, 3, 4,... is the set of _____ numbers.

5.   The number 36,205 is expressed in _____ notation.

## GUIDED EXAMPLES AND PRACTICE

**Objective A    Give the meaning of digits in standard notation.**

**Review these examples for Objective A:**
1.   What does the digit 7 mean in 4,678,952?

   4,6⬚7⬚8,952        7 ten thousands

2.   In 816,304,259, which digit tells the number of hundreds?

   816,304,⬚2⬚59
   The digit 2 tells the number of hundreds.

**Practice these exercises:**
1.   What does the 2 mean in 516,204?

2.   In 124,806,357, which digit tells the number of ten thousands?

**Objective B    Convert from standard notation to expanded notation.**

**Review this example for Objective B:**

**3.**  Write expanded notation for 12,309.

    12,309 = 1 ten thousand + 2 thousands
+ 3 hundreds + 0 tens + 9 ones, or 1 ten thousand
+ 2 thousands + 3 hundreds + 9 ones

**Practice this exercise:**

**3.**  Write expanded notation for 2087.

**Objective C    Convert between standard notation and word names.**

**Review these examples for Objective C:**

**4.**  Write the word name for 36,760,235.

The first period denotes millions. There are thirty-six millions. The second period denotes thousands. There are seven hundred sixty thousands. The last period denotes ones. There are two hundred thirty-five ones.
Thus, a word name for 36,760,235 is
thirty-six million, seven hundred sixty thousand, two hundred thirty-five.

**5.**  Write standard notation for eighty-six million, one hundred twenty-three thousand, seven hundred sixty-one.

The number named in the millions period is 86, the number named in the thousands period is 123, and the number named in the ones period is 761. We write each of these numbers in order, separating them with commas. Thus, standard notation is 86,123,761.

**Practice these exercises:**

**4.**  Write a word name for 5,487,203.

**5.**  Write standard notation for four hundred sixty-five thousand, eight hundred thirteen.

**ADDITIONAL EXERCISES**
**Objective A    Give the meaning of digits in standard notation.**
**For extra help**, see Examples 1–7 on pages 2–3 of your text and the Section 1.1 lecture video.
*What does the digit 8 mean in each number?*

**1.**  231,708

**2.**  897,435

*In the number 5,643,970, what digit names the number of:*

**3.**  hundreds?

**4.**  ten thousands?

**Objective B   Convert from standard notation to expanded notation.**
**For extra help**, see Examples 8–10 on page 4 of your text and the Section 1.1 lecture video.
*Write expanded notation for each number.*

**5.**  1813                          **6.**  7406


**7.**  85,126                        **8.**  653, 497


**9.**  4,306,749


**Objective C   Convert between standard notation and word names.**
**For extra help**, see Examples 11–15 on page 5 of your text and the Section 1.1 lecture video.
*Write a word name.*

**10.** 3452                          **11.** 77,422


*Write standard notation.*

**12.** One thousand, two hundred sixty-three    **13.** Four hundred fourteen thousand,
                                                       nine hundred sixty-three


**14.** Three billion

# Chapter 1 WHOLE NUMBERS

## 1.2 Addition

**Learning Objectives**
A    Add whole numbers.
B    Use addition in finding perimeter.

**Key Terms**
Use the vocabulary terms listed below to complete each statement in Exercises 1–2.

**commutative law of addition          associative law of addition**

1.    The statement $2 + 5 = 5 + 2$ illustrates the _____ .

2.    The statement $(2 + 5) + 3 = 2 + (5 + 3)$ illustrates the _____ .

## GUIDED EXAMPLES AND PRACTICE

### Objective A    Add whole numbers.

**Review this example for Objective A:**
1.    Add: $8429 + 4098$.

          1  1
     8 4 2 9
  + 4 0 9 8
  1 2, 5 2 7

We add ones. We get 17, so we have 1 ten + 7 ones. Write 7 in the ones column and 1 above the tens. We add tens. We get 12 tens, so we have 1 hundred and 2 tens. Write 2 in the tens column and 1 above the hundreds.
We add hundreds. We get 5.
We add thousands. We get 12.

**Practice this exercise:**
1.    Add: $27,609 + 38,415$.

### Objective B    Use addition in finding perimeter.

**Review this example for Objective B:**
2.    Find the perimeter.

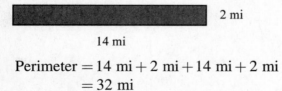

14 mi

Perimeter $= 14$ mi $+ 2$ mi $+ 14$ mi $+ 2$ mi
              $= 32$ mi

**Practice this exercise:**
2.    Find the perimeter.
56 in.

22 in.

**ADDITIONAL EXERCISES**
**Objective A    Add whole numbers.**
**For extra help**, see Examples 1–2 on pages 9–10 of your text and the Section 1.2 lecture video.
*Add.*

1.  
```
   9 5
 + 8 6
```

2.   5346 + 784

3.  
```
   1 9
   3 6
   7 8
 + 5 4
```

4.  
```
   1 3,4 7 3
      4,5 1 9
 +    7,3 9 5
```

**Objective B    Use addition in finding perimeter.**
**For extra help**, see Examples 3–4 on page 11 of your text and the Section 1.2 lecture video.
*Find the perimeter of each figure.*

5.

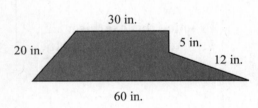

6.

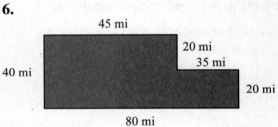

7.

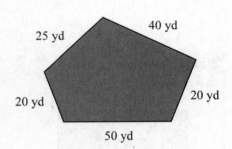

8.

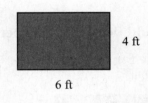

# Chapter 1 WHOLE NUMBERS

## 1.3 Subtraction

| **Learning Objectives** |
| --- |
| A    Subtract whole numbers. |

**Key Terms**

Use the vocabulary terms listed below to complete each statement in Exercises 1–2.

**difference**             **subtrahend**

1. In a subtraction sentence, the number being subtracted is the _____ .

2. The _____ $a - b$ is that unique number $c$ for which $a = c + b$.

## GUIDED EXAMPLES AND PRACTICE

**Objective A    Subtract whole numbers.**

**Review this example for Objective A:**

1. Subtract: $8045 - 2897$.

$$
\begin{array}{r}
7 \quad 9 \quad \overset{13}{\cancel{3}} \quad 15 \\
\cancel{8} \; \cancel{0} \; \cancel{4} \; \cancel{5} \\
- \; 2 \; 8 \; 9 \; 7 \\
\hline
5 \; 1 \; 4 \; 8
\end{array}
$$

We cannot subtract 7 ones from from 5 ones.
We borrow 1 ten to get 15 ones.
We cannot subtract 9 tens from 4 tens.
We borrow 1 hundred to get 13 tens.
We have 79 hundreds.

**Practice this exercise:**

1. Subtract: $6401 - 3629$.

## ADDITIONAL EXERCISES

**Objective A    Multiply whole numbers.**

**For extra help**, see Examples 1–7 on pages 14–16 of your text and the Section 1.3 lecture video.

*Subtract.*

1.     7 6 4
    $-$ 5 3 1

2.   $524 - 139$

**3.**  9352
       −6418


**4.**  32,156
       −  3,492


**5.**  6005
       −1456

# Chapter 1 WHOLE NUMBERS

## 1.4 Multiplication

**Learning Objectives**
A    Multiply whole numbers.
B    Use multiplication in finding area.

**Key Terms**
Use the vocabulary terms listed below to complete each statement in Exercises 1–3.

> **associative law of multiplication**          **commutative law of multiplication**
> **distributive law**

1.   The sentence $2 \cdot (3+5) = (2 \cdot 3) + (2 \cdot 5)$ illustrates the _____ .

2.   The sentence $2 \cdot 3 = 3 \cdot 2$ illustrates the _____ .

3.   The sentence $2 \cdot (3 \cdot 5) = (2 \cdot 3) \cdot 5$ illustrates the _____ .

## GUIDED EXAMPLES AND PRACTICE

### Objective A    Multiply whole numbers.

**Review this example for Objective A:**
1.   Multiply: $37 \times 415$.

$$
\begin{array}{r}
\phantom{\times 3}\overset{1}{\phantom{5}} \phantom{5} \\
\overset{1}{\phantom{4}}\ \overset{3}{\phantom{1}}\phantom{5} \\
4\ 1\ 5 \\
\times\ \ 3\ 7 \\
\hline
2\ 9\ 0\ 5 \\
1\ 2\ 4\ 5\ 0 \\
\hline
1\ 5,\ 3\ 5\ 5
\end{array}
$$

$\leftarrow$ Multiplying 415 by 7
$\leftarrow$ Multiplying 415 by 30

**Practice this exercise:**
1.   Multiply: $238 \times 764$.

### Objective B    Use multiplication in finding area.

**Review this example for Objective B:**
2.   Find the area.

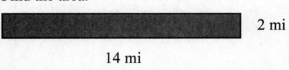

2 mi

14 mi

$A = l \cdot w = 14 \text{ mi} \cdot 2 \text{ mi} = 28 \text{ sq mi}$

**Practice this exercise:**
2.   Find the area.

13 in.

13 in.

**ADDITIONAL EXERCISES**
**Objective A    Multiply whole numbers.**
**For extra help**, see Examples 1–4 on pages 20–22 of your text and the Section 1.4 lecture video.
*Multiply.*

1.    4 3
     × 6

2.    43(62)

3.    2 9 3
     × 5 4 7

4.    8 0 4 2
     × 7 6 3 3

**Objective B    Use multiplication in finding area.**
**For extra help**, see Example 5 on page 23 of your text and the Section 1.4 lecture video.
*Find the area of each figure.*

5.
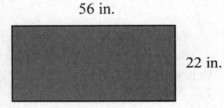
56 in.

22 in.

6.
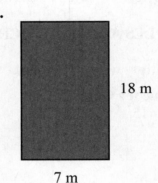
18 m

7 m

7.
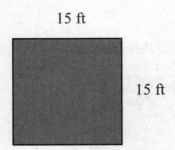
15 ft

15 ft

# Chapter 1 WHOLE NUMBERS

## 1.5 Division

| Learning Objectives |
| --- |
| A    Divide whole numbers. |

## Key Terms

Use the vocabulary terms listed below to complete each statement in Exercises 1–4.

**one**          **zero**          **not defined**          **that same number**

1. Zero divided by any nonzero number is _____ .

2. Any number divided by 1 is _____ .

3. Division by 0 is _____ .

4. Any nonzero number divided by itself is _____ .

## GUIDED EXAMPLES AND PRACTICE

**Objective A    Divide whole numbers.**

**Review this example for Objective A:**
1.    Divide: $8973 \div 36$.

```
        249
   36)8973
        72↓      Bring down the 7
       177
       144↓      Bring down the 3
        333
        324
          9      The remainder is 9.
```

The answer is 249 R 9.

**Practice this exercise:**
1.    Divide: $8519 \div 27$.

**ADDITIONAL EXERCISES**

**Objective A    Divide whole numbers.**

**For extra help**, see Examples 1–5 on pages 27–31 of your text and the Section 1.5 lecture video.

*Divide, if possible. If not possible, write "not defined."*

**1.**   $\dfrac{42}{1}$

**2.**   $45 \div 0$

*Divide.*

**3.**   $738 \div 6$

**4.**   $5\overline{)948}$

**5.**   $24\overline{)2592}$

# Chapter 1 WHOLE NUMBERS

## 1.6 Rounding and Estimating; Order

**Learning Objectives**
A    Round to the nearest ten, hundred, or thousand.
B    Estimate sums, differences, products, and quotients by rounding.
C    Use < or > for ☐ to write a true sentence in a situation like 6 ☐ 10 .

**Key Terms**
Use the vocabulary terms listed below to complete each statement in Exercises 1–2.

**equation**                    **inequality**

1.    A sentence like 2 + 3 = 5 is an _____ .

2.    A sentence like 2 < 3 is an _____ .

## GUIDED EXAMPLES AND PRACTICE

**Objective A    Round to the nearest ten, hundred, or thousand.**

**Review this example for Objective A:**
1.    Round 8365 to the nearest hundred.

a) Locate the digit in the hundreds place, 3.
    8365
       ↑

b) Consider the next digit to the right, 6.
    8365
       ↑

c) Since that digit, 6, is 5 or higher, round 3 hundreds up to 4 hundreds.
d) Change all digits to the right of the hundreds digit to zeros.
    8400   ←  This is the answer.

**Practice this exercise:**
1.    Round 27,459 to the nearest thousand.

**Objective B   Estimate sums, differences, products, and quotients by rounding.**

<table>
<tr><td>

**Review these examples for Objective B:**

2.  Estimate this sum by first rounding to the nearest ten: 84 + 35 + 49 + 22.

```
    8 4      8 0
    3 5      4 0
    4 9      5 0
  + 2 2    + 2 0
           ─────
           1 9 0   ← Estimated answer
```

3.  Estimate this difference by first rounding to the nearest hundred: 7546 – 3271.

```
   7 5 4 6     7 5 0 0
 − 3 2 7 1   − 3 3 0 0
             ─────────
               4 2 0 0   ← Estimated answer
```

4.  Estimate this product by first rounding to the nearest thousand: $4532 \times 8291$.

```
    4 5 3 2        5 0 0 0
  × 8 2 9 1      × 8 0 0 0
               ────────────
               40,000,000   ← Estimated answer
```

5.  Estimate this quotient by first rounding to the nearest thousand: $41,624 \div 5803$.

```
                      7
5803)41,624    6000)42,000
                    42,000
                    ──────
                         0
```

</td><td>

**Practice these exercises:**

2.  Estimate this sum by first rounding to the nearest thousand.

```
    2 7 6 4
    9 0 7 6
  + 4 5 2 8
```

3.  Estimate this difference by first rounding to the nearest hundred.

```
    6 3 2 8
  − 4 2 9 1
```

4.  Estimate this product by first rounding to the nearest ten.

```
      2 3
    × 7 7
```

5.  Estimate this quotient by first rounding to the nearest hundred: $3472 \div 670$.

</td></tr>
</table>

**Objective C   Use < or > for ☐ to write a true sentence in a situation like 6 ☐ 10.**

<table>
<tr><td>

**Review this example for Objective C:**

6.  *Use < or > for* ☐ *to write a true sentence:*
    23 ☐ 16.

    Since 23 is to the right of 16 on a number line, 23 > 16.

</td><td>

**Practice this exercise:**

6.  *Use < or > for* ☐ *to write a true sentence:* 33 ☐ 36.

</td></tr>
</table>

## ADDITIONAL EXERCISES
**Objective A    Round to the nearest ten, hundred, or thousand.**
**For extra help**, see Examples 1–7 on pages 37–39 of your text and the Section 1.6 lecture video.

1.  Round 763 to the nearest ten.

2.  Round 3063 to the nearest hundred.

3.  Round 65,812 to the nearest thousand.

**Objective B    Estimate sums, differences, products, and quotients by rounding.**
**For extra help**, see Examples 8–13 on pages 39–42 of your text and the Section 1.6 lecture video.

4.  Estimate this sum by first rounding to the nearest ten: $51 + 67 + 29 + 43$.

5.  Estimate this difference by first rounding to the nearest hundred: $6783 - 4246$.

6.  Estimate this product by first rounding to the nearest hundred: $870 \times 209$.

7.  Estimate this quotient by first rounding to the nearest ten: $278 \div 72$.

8.  Movie rentals cost $4.95 each. The total movie rental sales for Tuesday was $905.85. Estimate the number of movies rented for Tuesday.

**Objective C**  Use < or > for ☐ to write a true sentence in a situation like 6 ☐ 10.
**For extra help,** see Examples 14–15 on page 43 of your text and the Section 1.6 lecture video.

*Use < or > for* ☐ *to write a true sentence. Draw the number line if necessary.*

**9.**  51 ☐ 37

**10.**  134 ☐ 143

**11.**  216 ☐ 202

**12.**  1098 ☐ 1046

# Chapter 1 WHOLE NUMBERS

## 1.7 Solving Equations

---

**Learning Objectives**
A   Solve simple equations by trial.
B   Solve equations like $x + 28 = 54$, $28 \cdot x = 168$, and $98 \cdot 2 = y$.

---

**Key Terms**
Use the vocabulary terms listed below to complete each statement in Exercises 1–3.

      **equation**         **solution of an equation**        **variable**

1.   A(n) _____ is a replacement for the variable that makes the equation true.

2.   A(n) _____ is a sentence with =.

3.   A(n) _____ can represent any number.

## GUIDED EXAMPLES AND PRACTICE

**Objective A   Solve simple equations by trial.**

**Review this example for Objective A:**
1.   Solve $x + 5 = 12$ by trial.

We replace $x$ with several numbers.

If we replace $x$ with 5, we get a false equation:
$5 + 5 = 12$.
If we replace $x$ with 6, we get a false equation:
$6 + 5 = 12$.
If we replace $x$ with 7, we get a true equation:
$7 + 5 = 12$.

No other replacement makes the equation true, so the solution is 7.

**Practice this exercise:**
1.   Solve $x - 2 = 6$ by trial.

**Objective B   Solve equations like $x + 28 = 54$, $28 \cdot x = 168$, and $98 \cdot 2 = y$.**

**Review these examples for Objective B:**
2.   Solve $t + 15 = 32$.

$$\begin{aligned}
t + 15 &= 32 \\
t + 15 - 15 &= 32 - 15 \quad \text{Subtracting 15 on both sides} \\
t + 0 &= 17 \\
t &= 17
\end{aligned}$$

The solution is 17.

**Practice these exercises:**
2.   Solve $y + 8 = 9$.

**3.** Solve $x = 156 \times 18$.

To solve the equation, we carry out the calculation.

$$
\begin{array}{r}
1\ 5\ 6 \\
\times\ \ 1\ 8 \\
\hline
1\ 2\ 4\ 8 \\
1\ 5\ 6\ 0 \\
\hline
2\ 8\ 0\ 8
\end{array}
\qquad
\begin{array}{l}
x = 156 \times 18 \\
x = 2808
\end{array}
$$

The solution is 2808.

**3.** Solve $46 \times 61 = n$.

**4.** Solve $16 \cdot n = 416$.

$$16 \cdot n = 416$$
$$\frac{16 \cdot n}{16} = \frac{416}{16} \quad \text{Dividing by 16 on both sides}$$
$$n = 26$$

The solution is 26.

**4.** Solve $24 \cdot y = 912$.

## ADDITIONAL EXERCISES
**Objective A    Solve simple equations by trial.**
**For extra help**, see Examples 1–3 on page 48 of your text and the Section 1.7 lecture video.
*Solve by trial.*

**1.**  $y - 5 = 8$

**2.**  $x + 3 = 7$

**3.**  $48 \div 6 = t$

**4.**  $x \cdot 13 = 26$

**Objective B    Solve equations like $x + 28 = 54$, $28 \cdot x = 168$, and $98 \cdot 2 = y$.**
**For extra help**, see Examples 4–11 on pages 48–51 of your text and the Section 1.7 lecture video.
*Solve. Be sure to check.*

**5.**  $108 \div 9 = w$

**6.**  $7 + x = 42$

**7.**  $150 = 6 \cdot y$

**8.**  $8001 - 1469 = x$

# Chapter 1 WHOLE NUMBERS

## 1.8 Applications and Problem Solving

---
**Learning Objectives**
A   Solve applied problems involving addition, subtraction, multiplication, or division of whole numbers.
---

**Key Terms**
Use the vocabulary terms listed below to complete each statement in Exercises 1–2.

   **translate the problem to an equation        familiarize yourself with the situation**

1.   The first step in solving an applied problem is to _____ .

2.   The second step in solving an applied problem is to _____ .

## GUIDED EXAMPLES AND PRACTICE

**Objective A   Solve applied problems involving addition, subtraction, multiplication, or division of whole numbers.**

**Review this example for Objective A:**
1.   Margaret borrows $8820 to buy a car. The loan is to be paid off in 36 equal monthly payments. How much is each payment (excluding interest)?

   1. *Familiarize.* Visualize a rectangular array of dollar bills with 36 rows. How many dollars are in each row?
   Let $p$ = the amount of each payment.
   2. *Translate.* We translate to an equation.

| Amount of loan | divided by | Number of payments | is | Amount of each payment |
|:---:|:---:|:---:|:---:|:---:|
| ↓ | ↓ | ↓ | ↓ | ↓ |
| 8820 | ÷ | 36 | = | $p$ |

**Practice this exercise:**
1.   Rex is driving from Las Vegas to Chicago, a distance of 1749 miles. He travels 1399 miles to Des Moines. How much farther must he travel?

3. *Solve*. We carry out the division.

$$\begin{array}{r} 245 \\ 36\overline{)8820} \\ \underline{72} \\ 162 \\ \underline{144} \\ 180 \\ \underline{180} \\ 0 \end{array}$$

4. *Check*. We can repeat the calculation. We can also multiply the number of payments by the amount of each payment: $36 \cdot 245 = 8820$. The answer checks.

5. *State*. Each payment is $245.

## ADDITIONAL EXERCISES
**Objective A    Solve applied problems involving addition, subtraction, multiplication, or division of whole numbers.**
**For extra help**, see Examples 1–8 on pages 54–61 of your text and the Section 1.8 lecture video.
*Solve.*

1. In her job as a telemarketer, Jody contacted 952 customers in September, 1058 customers in October, 857 customers in November, and 1314 customers in December. What was the total number of customers contacted?

2. Donna's car gets 26 miles to the gallon in city driving. How many gallons will she use in 1092 miles of city driving?

3. Hudson Manufacturing buys 315 office chairs at $160 each for use at its new corporate headquarters. Find the total cost of the purchase.

4. In 2004, there were 773,200 jobs in the home healthcare industry. It is estimated that there will be 1,310,300 jobs in this industry in 2014. Find the increase in jobs from 2004 to 2014.

Name:                          Date:
Instructor:                    Section:

# Chapter 1 WHOLE NUMBERS

### 1.9 Exponential Notation and Order of Operations

**Learning Objectives**
A   Write exponential notation for products such as $4 \cdot 4 \cdot 4$.
B   Evaluate exponential notation.
C   Simplify expressions using the rules for order of operations.
D   Remove parentheses within parentheses.

**Key Terms**
Use the vocabulary terms listed below to complete each statement in Exercises 1–3.

    **average**              **base**             **exponent**

1.   In the expression $5^3$, 3 is the _____ .

2.   In the expression $5^3$, 5 is the _____ .

3.   The _____ of a set of numbers is the sum of the numbers divided by the number of addends.

## GUIDED EXAMPLES AND PRACTICE

**Objective A   Write exponential notation for products such as $4 \cdot 4 \cdot 4$.**

**Review this example for Objective A:**
1.   Write exponential notation for $6 \cdot 6 \cdot 6 \cdot 6$.

    Exponential notation is $6^4$.

**Practice this exercise:**
1.   Write exponential notation for $2 \cdot 2 \cdot 2 \cdot 2 \cdot 2$.

**Objective B   Evaluate exponential notation.**

**Review this example for Objective B:**
2.   Evaluate: $3^4$.

    $3^4 = 3 \cdot 3 \cdot 3 \cdot 3 = 81$

**Practice this exercise:**
2.   Evaluate $5^3$.

**Objective C    Simplify expressions using the rules for order of operations.**

**Review this example for Objective C:**

3.  Simplify: $64 \div 4^2 \cdot 3 + (12 - 7)$.

$64 \div 4^2 \cdot 3 + (12 - 7)$
$= 64 \div 4^2 \cdot 3 + (5)$  Subtracting inside parentheses
$= 64 \div 16 \cdot 3 + 5$  Evaluating exponential expressions
$= 4 \cdot 3 + 5$  Doing all multiplications,
$= 12 + 5$  divisions, and additions in
$= 17$  order from left to right

4.  Find the average of 12, 32, 15, and 29.

The number of addends is 4, so we divide the sum of the numbers by 4.
The average is given by
$$\frac{12 + 32 + 15 + 29}{4} = \frac{88}{4} = 22 .$$

**Practice this exercise:**

3.  Simplify: $9 + (19 - 9)^2 \div 5 \cdot 2$.

4.  Find the average of 43, 26, 35, and 16.

**Objective D    Remove parentheses within parentheses.**

**Review this example for Objective D:**

5.  Simplify: $7 + \{15 - [2 \times (6 - 4)]\}$.

$7 + \{15 - [2 \times (6 - 4)]\}$
$= 7 + \{15 - [2 \times 2]\}$  Doing the calculations in the innermost parentheses first
$= 7 + \{15 - 4\}$  Again, doing the calculations in the innermost brackets
$= 7 + 11$  Subtracting inside the braces
$= 18$  Adding

**Practice this exercise:**

5.  Simplify
$25 + \{3 \times [18 - (2 + 6)]\}$.

## ADDITIONAL EXERCISES

**Objective A    Write exponential notation for products such as $4 \cdot 4 \cdot 4$.**

**For extra help**, see Examples 1–2 on page 71 of your text and the Section 1.9 lecture video.
*Write exponential notation.*

1.  $8 \cdot 8 \cdot 8 \cdot 8 \cdot 8$

2.  $4 \cdot 4 \cdot 4$

3.  $5 \cdot 5 \cdot 5 \cdot 5$

4.  $6 \cdot 6 \cdot 6 \cdot 6 \cdot 6 \cdot 6 \cdot 6$

## Objective B    Evaluate exponential notation.
**For extra help**, see Examples 3–4 on page 72 of your text and the Section 1.9 lecture video.
*Evaluate.*

**5.**  $2^7$

**6.**  $3^5$

**7.**  $6^3$

**8.**  $10^2$

## Objective C    Simplify expressions using the rules for order of operations.
**For extra help**, see Examples 5–12 on pages 73–74 of your text and the Section 1.9 lecture video.
*Simplify.*

**9.**  $5 \cdot 9 + 30$

**10.**  $100 - 5 \cdot 5 - 2$

**11.**  $4^3 - 5 \times 3 - (4 + 2 \cdot 7)$

**12.**  $15(6 - 4)^2 - 3(2 + 1)^2$

**13.**  Find the average of 67, 70, 39, and 56.

**Objective D   Remove parentheses within parentheses.**
**For extra help**, see Examples 13–14 on page 76 of your text and the Section 1.9 lecture video.
*Evaluate.*

**14.** $[28 - (2+6) \div 2] - [24 \div (5+1)]$

**15.** $8 \times \{(31-9) \cdot [(17+23) \div 4 - (6-3)]\}$

**16.** $9 \times 20 - \{50 \div [12 - (4+3)]\}$

**17.** $64 \div 4 - [3 \times (10 - 4 \cdot 2)]$

**18.** $[56 \times (5-3) \div 8] + [6 \times (7-1)]$

# Complete Answers

## Chapter 1 WHOLE NUMBERS

### Section 1.1

#### Key Terms
1. expanded
2. whole
3. digit
4. natural
5. standard

#### Practice
1. 2 hundreds
2. 0
3. 2 thousands + 0 hundreds + 8 tens + 7 ones, or 2 thousands + 8 tens + 7 ones
4. Five million, four hundred eighty-seven thousand, two hundred three
5. 465,813

#### Objective A
1. 8 ones
2. 8 hundred thousands
3. 9
4. 4

#### Objective B
5. 1 thousand + 8 hundreds + 1 ten + 3 ones
6. 7 thousands + 4 hundreds + 0 tens + 6 ones, or 7 thousands + 4 hundreds + 6 ones
7. 8 ten thousands + 5 thousands + 1 hundred + 2 tens + 6 ones
8. 6 hundred thousands + 5 ten thousands + 3 thousands + 4 hundreds + 9 tens + 7 ones
9. 4 millions + 3 hundred thousands + 0 ten thousands + 6 thousands + 7 hundreds + 4 tens + 9 ones, or 4 millions + 3 hundred thousands + 6 thousands + 7 hundreds + 4 tens + 9 ones

#### Objective C
10. Three thousand, four hundred fifty-two
11. Seventy-seven thousand, four hundred twenty-two
12. 1263
13. 414,963
14. 3,000,000,000

### Section 1.2

#### Key Terms
1. commutative law of addition
2. associative law of addition

#### Practice
1. 66,024
2. 156 in.

**Objective A**
1. 181
2. 6130
3. 187
4. 25,387

**Objective B**
5. 127 in.
6. 240 mi
7. 155 yd
8. 20 ft

## Section 1.3

**Key Terms**
1. subtrahend
2. difference

**Practice**
1. 2772

**Objective A**
1. 233
2. 385
3. 2934
4. 28,664
5. 4549

## Section 1.4

**Key Terms**
1. distributive law
2. commutative law of multiplication
3. associative law of multiplication

**Practice**
1. 181,832
2. 169 sq in.

**Objective A**
1. 258
2. 2666
3. 160,271
4. 61,384,586

**Objective B**
5. 1232 sq in.
6. 126 sq m
7. 225 sq ft

## Section 1.5

**Key Terms**
1. zero
2. that same number
3. not defined
4. one

**Practice**
1. 315 R 14

**Objective A**
1. 42
3. 123
5. 108

2. not defined
4. 189 R 3

## Section 1.6

**Key Terms**
1. equation

2. inequality

**Practice**
1. 27,000
3. 2000
5. 5

2. 17,000
4. 1600
6. <

**Objective A**
1. 760
3. 66,000

2. 3100

**Objective B**
4. 190
6. 180,000
8. 180 movie rentals

5. 2600
7. 4

**Objective C**
9. >
11. >

10. <
12. >

## Section 1.7

**Key Terms**
1. solution of an equation
3. variable

2. equation

**Practice**
1. 8
3. 2806

2. 1
4. 38

**Objective A**
1. 13
3. 8

2. 4
4. 2

**Objective B**
5. 12
7. 25
6. 35
8. 6532

## Section 1.8

**Key Terms**
1. familiarize yourself with the situation
2. translate the problem to an equation

**Practice**
1. 350 mi

**Objective A**
1. 4181 customers
3. $50,400
2. 42 gallons
4. 537,100 jobs

## Section 1.9

**Key Terms**
1. exponent
3. average
2. base

**Practice**
1. $2^5$
3. 49
5. 55
2. 125
4. 30

**Objective A**
1. $8^5$
3. $5^4$
2. $4^3$
4. $6^7$

**Objective B**
5. 128
7. 216
6. 243
8. 100

**Objective C**
9. 75
11. 31
13. 58
10. 73
12. 33

**Objective D**
14. 20
16. 170
18. 50
15. 1232
17. 10